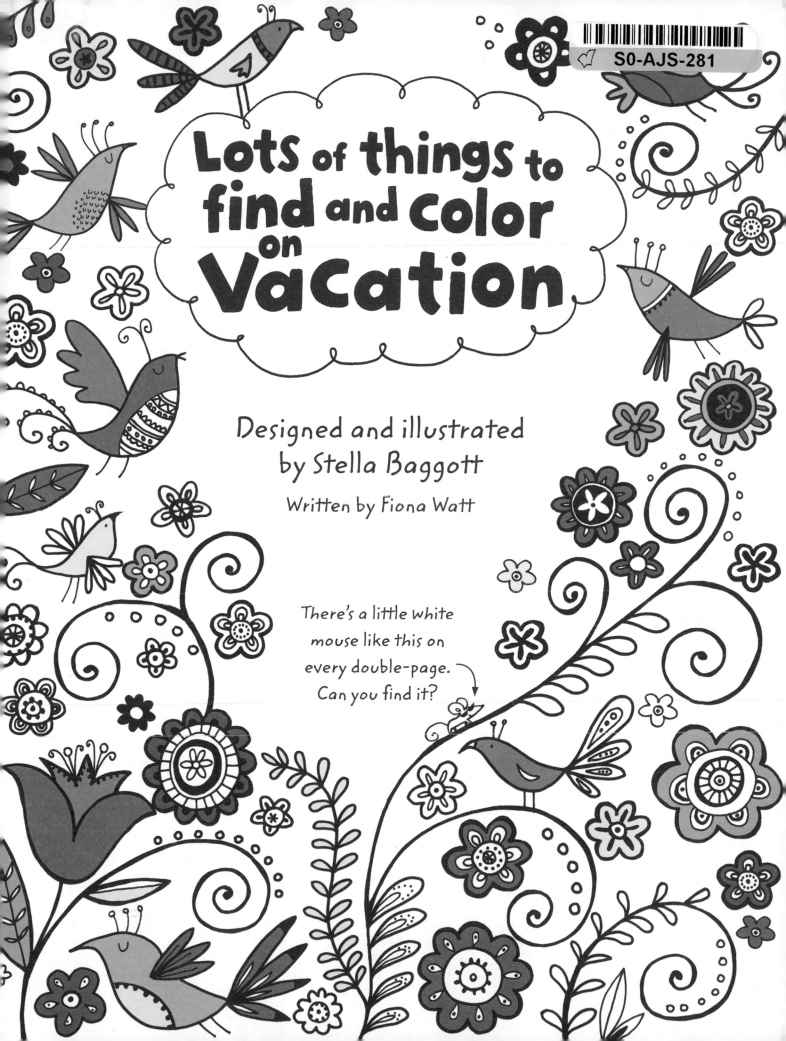

S0-AJS-281

Lots of things to find and color on Vacation

Designed and illustrated
by Stella Baggott

Written by Fiona Watt

There's a little white
mouse like this on
every double-page.
Can you find it?

Find another mouse holding a ball the same as this.

Can you find and color six kites?

Can you find five more mice eating watermelon?

Can you spot this mouse's twin?

4

Can you find another mouse with a green ring like this?

Spot the odd one out in each row and color it in.

Find the sea horse and color it in.

Color all the striped fish.

All the mermaids have a twin. Find each pair
and color them to match.

Find all the parachutes and color them red.

Find the pairs of planes and color them to match each other.

8

Can you spot a flying pig and color it pink?

Color all the birds blue.

9

Find four donkeys standing in the streets and color them brown.

Can you find all the taxis like this and color them yellow?

TAXI

TAXI

TAXI

10

There are four people standing near the edges of the pages. Draw lines showing the route they should take to reach the fiesta in the town square.

Find the buildings with bumpy roofs like this and color them in bright colors.

Spot the two birds that are the same and color them to match.

Find the birds with curly tail feathers and color them in.

12

Color all the flowers in bright colors.

Can you find a butterfly hiding between the flowers?

13

Draw a line to show the way the crab should go to get to the sea.

Find the starfish and color them yellow.

14

Find all the spotted fish and color them blue.

Find all the striped fish and color them orange.

Find all the fish with zigzags and color them green.

Spot the little octopus.

15

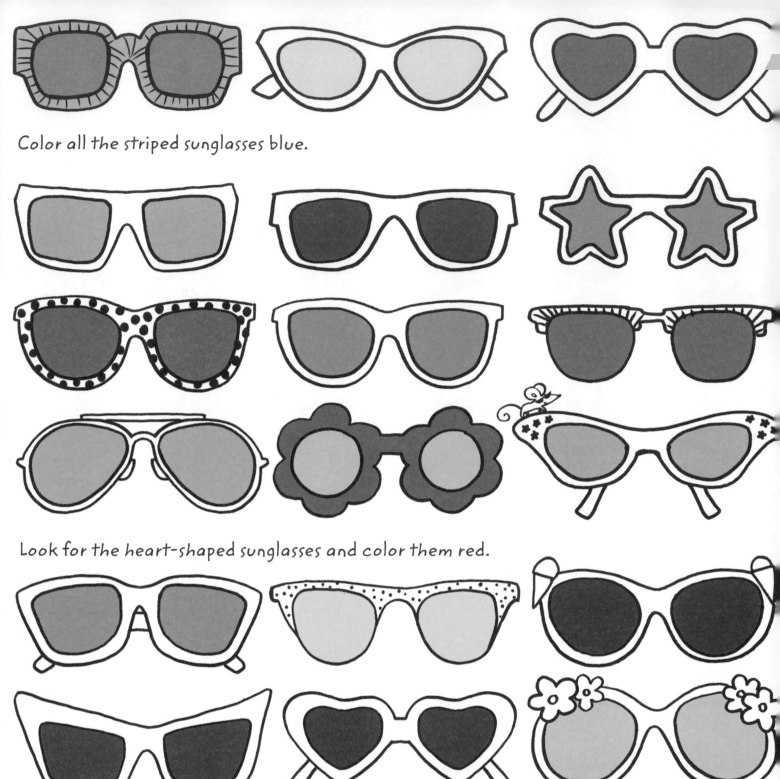

Color all the striped sunglasses blue.

Look for the heart-shaped sunglasses and color them red.

16

Can you find the sunglasses with palm trees on them? Color the trees green.

Color all the star-shaped sunglasses orange.

Find and color the birds.

Find the elephants with flowery patterns and color in the flowers.

18

Color in all the elephants' blankets.

Can you spot the sad baby elephant?

19

This bird has caught a worm, can you find five more?

Find five butterflies and color them blue.

Can you spot five birds wearing hats?

20

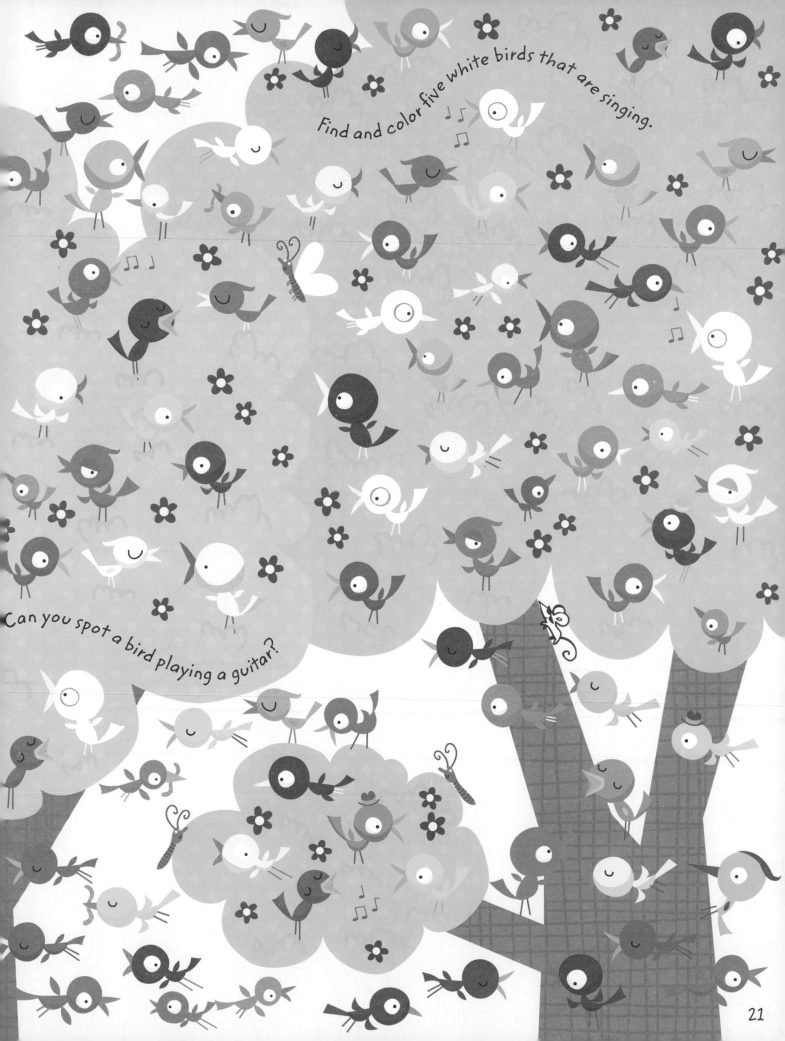

Find and color five white birds that are singing.

Can you spot a bird playing a guitar?

21

Look for the seahorses with spotted tummies and color them blue.

Find and color the fish yellow.

Find the baby seahorses with striped tails and color them red.

22

Look for the spotted jellyfish and color them purple.

Find the jellyfish with six legs and color them pink.

Color the striped jellyfish yellow.

Find all the seagulls with three fish and color the fish blue.

How many seagulls have no fish? Color their beaks orange.

24

Find the seagulls with two fish and color the fish green.

Can you spot the seagull who found a sandwich?

Find all ice cream cones with three scoops and color them pink.

Find all ice cream cones with cherries and color the cherries red.

Can you spot the melting ice cream? Color it in.

Find all ice cream cones with sprinkles and color them in chocolate brown.

Can you spot an ice cream wearing sunglasses?

Color all the Popsicles orange.

27

Find another mask identical to this and color it the same.

Look for another mask the same as this one and color it to match.

Find a mask identical to this and color it the same.

Can you spot a mask identical to this? Color it to match. ↗

Color the identical mask to this in the same colors.

Find another mask to match this one and color it the same. ↘

29

Spot the odd one out in each row and color it in.

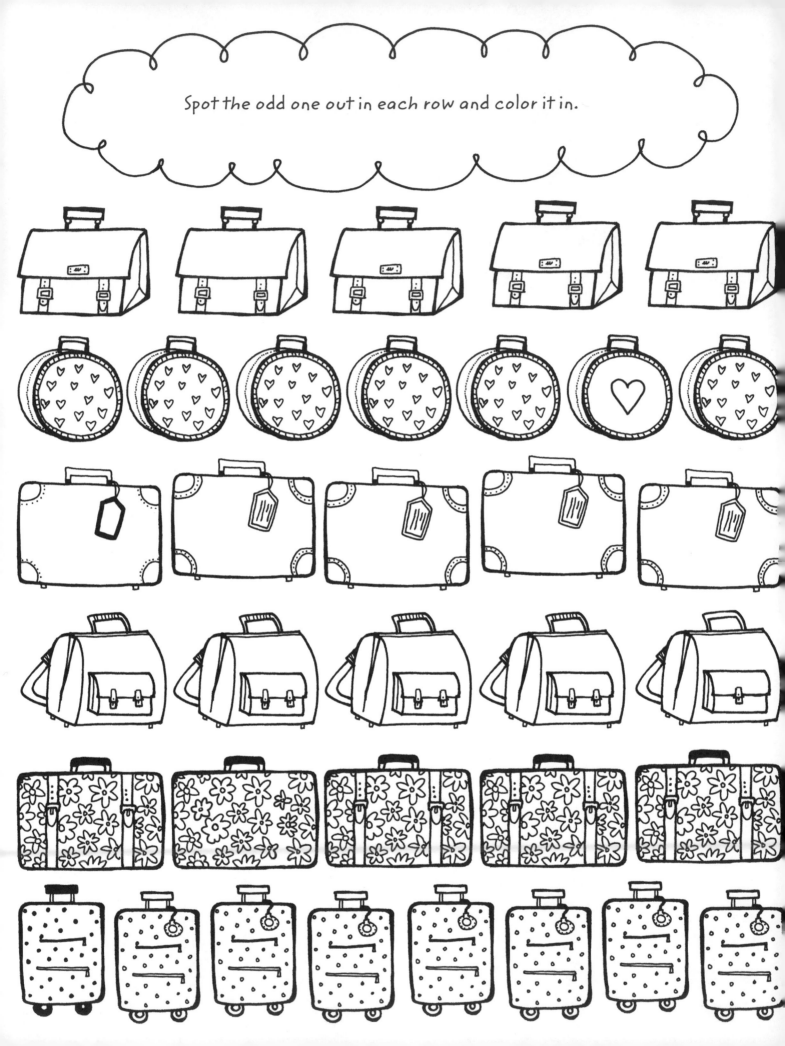

Find the koalas with white noses and fill the noses in black.

Can you spot a koala wearing sunglasses?

Look for the kookaburra birds and color them brown.

Find the baby koalas and color them gray.

31

Can you spot a turtle wearing sunglasses?

Find the turtles with five patches on their shells and color them blue.

32

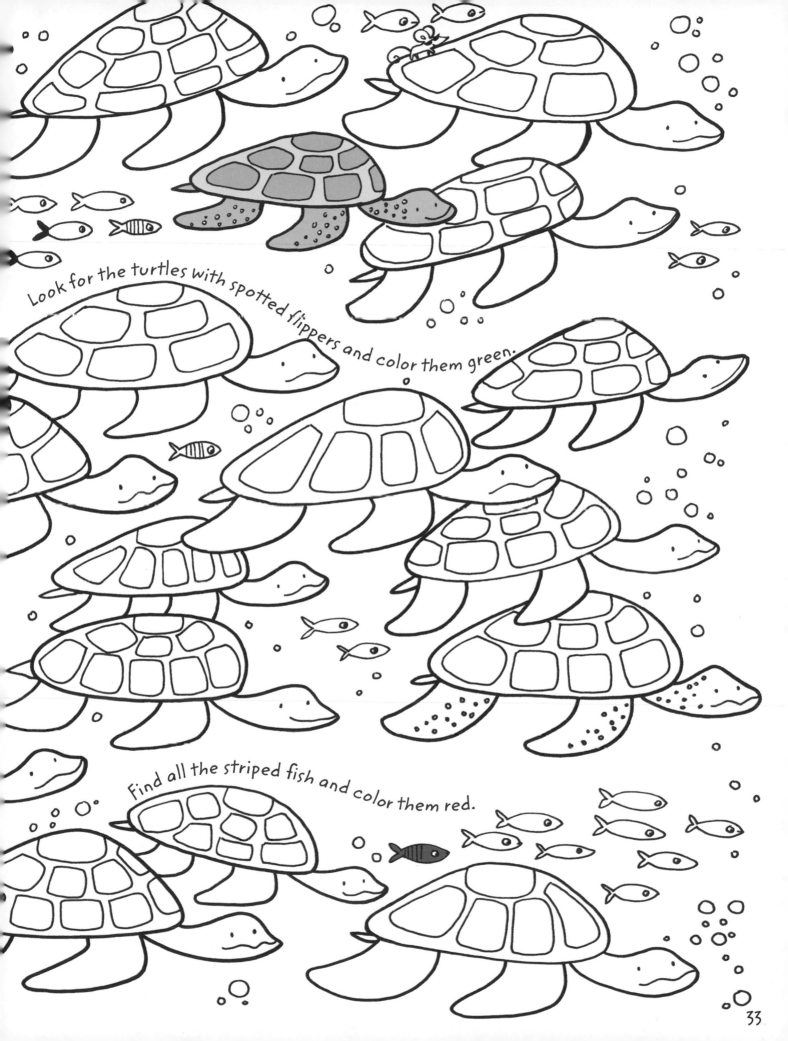

Look for the turtles with spotted flippers and color them green.

Find all the striped fish and color them red.

Can you find six cars like this with suitcases on the roof?

Spot six white trucks. Color them blue.

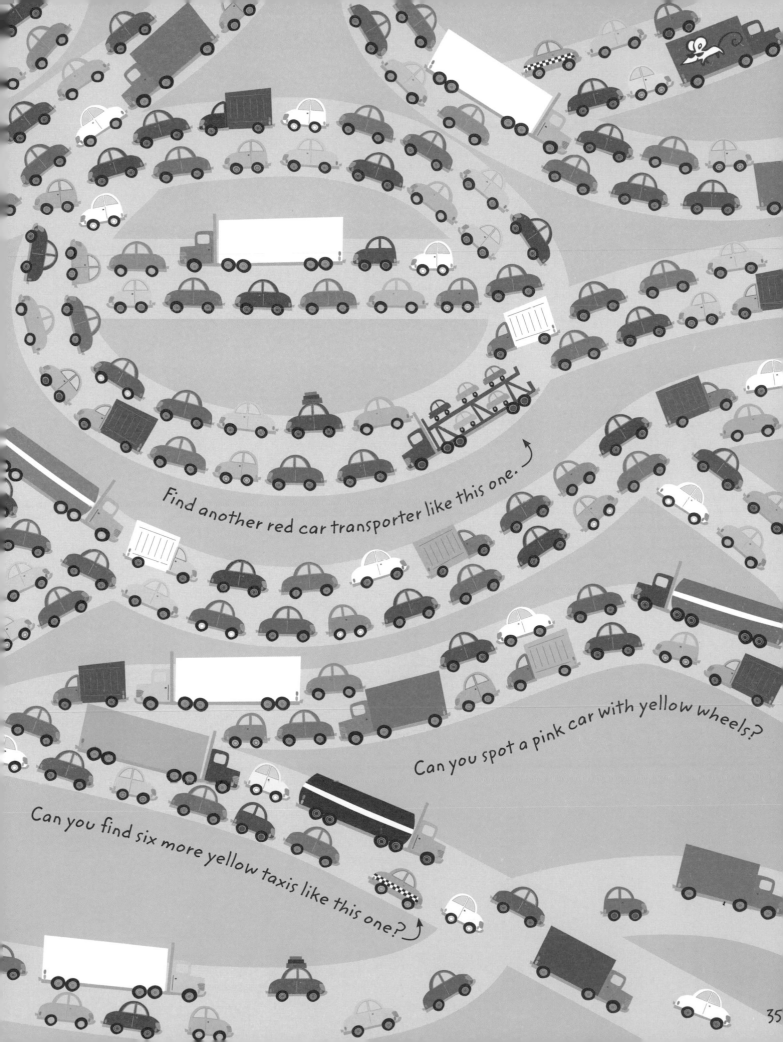

Find another red car transporter like this one.

Can you spot a pink car with yellow wheels?

Can you find six more yellow taxis like this one?

Can you find the seagull who has caught a crab? Color its beak yellow.

Find another boat the same as this and color it to match.

Can you spot a cat who has caught a fish?

Find the cat who has dropped its paddle and color it in.

37

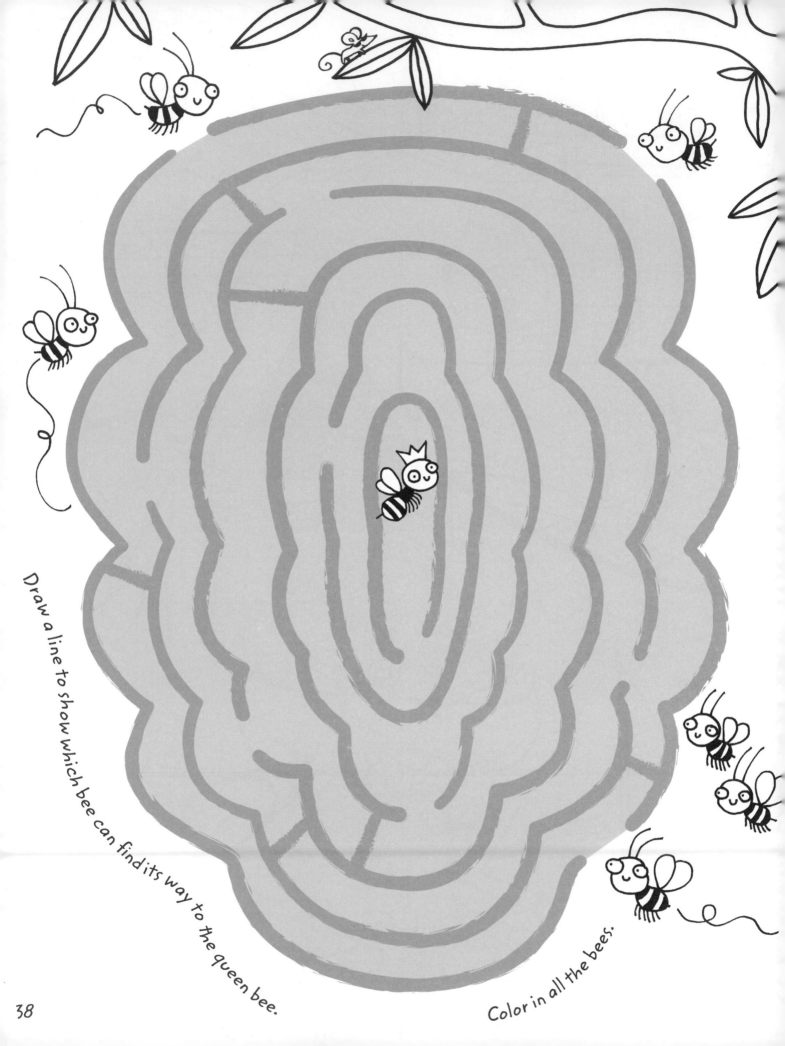

Draw a line to show which bee can find its way to the queen bee.

Color in all the bees.

38

Find six more bugs the same as this and color them yellow.

Look for five more bugs like this one and color them red.

Can you spot six more bugs that match this one? Color them orange.

39

Find the trees with four birds and color the birds in bright colors.

Look for a pear tree and color the pears green.

Find the bird who has caught a worm and color it in.

Color in all the trees with two birds.

Can you spot a tree that is a different shape than the others? Color it in.

Find the apple trees and color the apples red.

Find the stamp with a bucket and shovel on it and color it in.

Find five stamps with fruit and color them in.

Look for the stamps with butterflies and color them in.

Find five stamps with fish on them and color them in.

42

Can you find a stamp with a snake on it? Color it in.

Find all the empty stamps and draw your own pictures on them.

Find the stamp with a ladybug and color it red.

43

44

Find the pairs of beach shoes and color them to match.

Color in all the shells.

46

Spot the odd one out in each row and color it in.

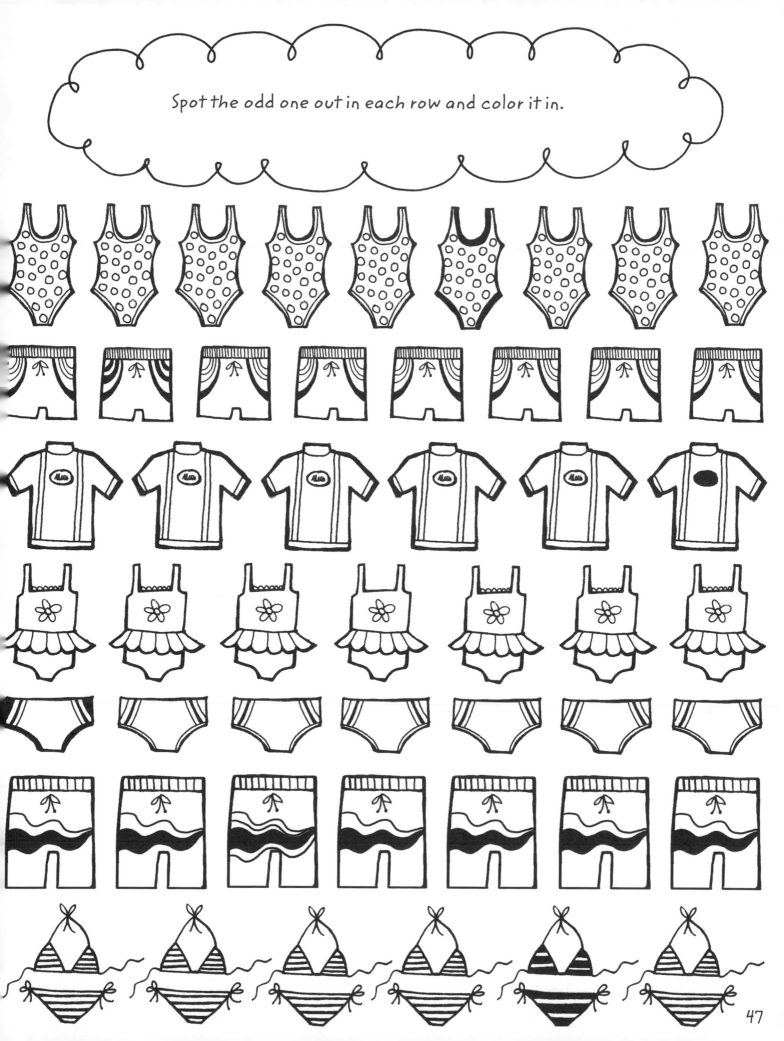

Look for a bug wearing boots. Color it red.

Find and color four more bugs like this one.

48

Can you spot a striped caterpillar?

Find five more caterpillars like this and color them.

49

Can you find five more fish like this?

Can you find five more seahorses like this?

Hunt for three orange crabs like this one.

50

Look for three more jellyfish like this.

Find all the plain white fish and color them in.

Can you spot a turtle?

51

Find all the butterflies that look like this and color them.

Search for more butterflies like this and color them.

Look for more butterflies like this and fill them in.

Find and color four more butterflies that look like this one.

Can you spot a ladybug? Color it red.

53

Spot the odd one out in each row and color it in.

Color in all the things that someone might take to the beach.

Find the monkey chasing a seagull and color in the monkey.

Color all the buckets blue.

Find all the monkeys eating ice cream and color them in.

Look for all the monkeys wearing sunglasses. Color in the monkeys.

Color all the sandcastles yellow.

Find all the kites and color them red.

Find six starfish like this one and color them orange.

Find five starfish like this one and color them purple.

58

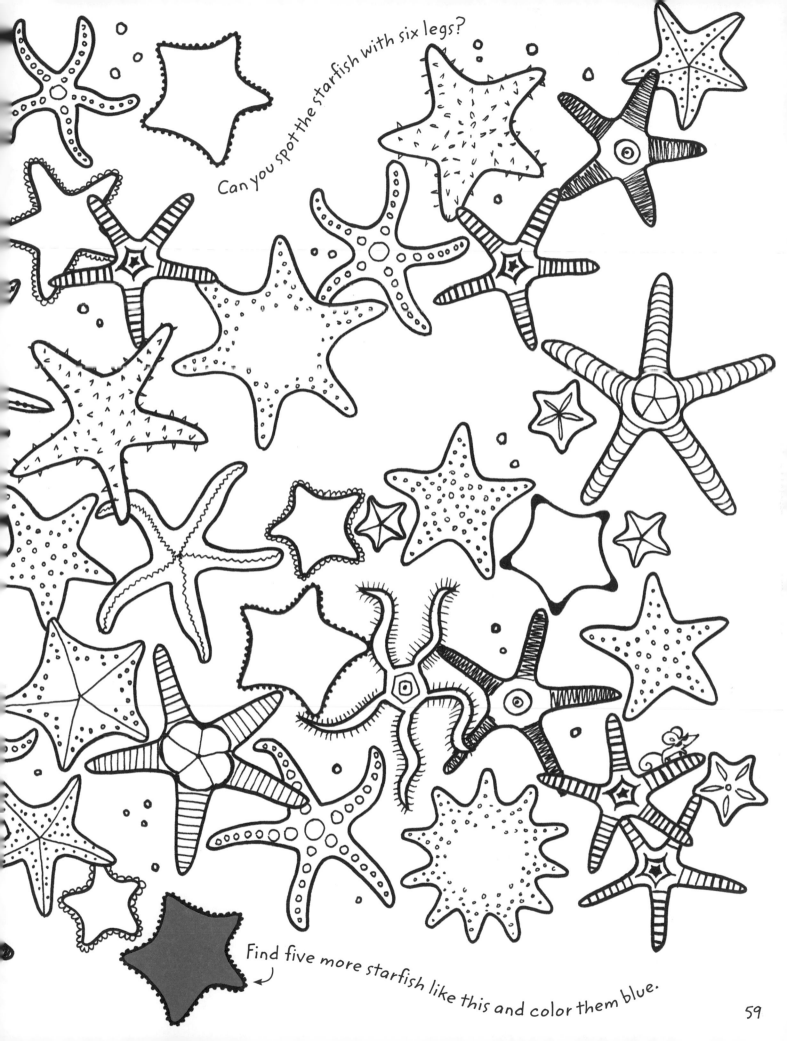

Can you spot the starfish with six legs?

Find five more starfish like this and color them blue.

Find the hermit crabs peeking out from their shells and color them orange.

Find and color the shells that have a crab hiding inside.

Find all the other crabs and color them red.

Can you spot a crab with only one claw? (Don't worry, it will grow a new one!)

Draw a line to show the way the fish must swim to get to her eggs.

Color all the baby fish orange.

Find the ice creams and color them pink.

Look for the fish and color them blue.

Spot all the crabs and color them red.

Find the cars with three suitcases on the roof and color the cars blue.

Can you find a pig wearing sunglasses? Color it pink.

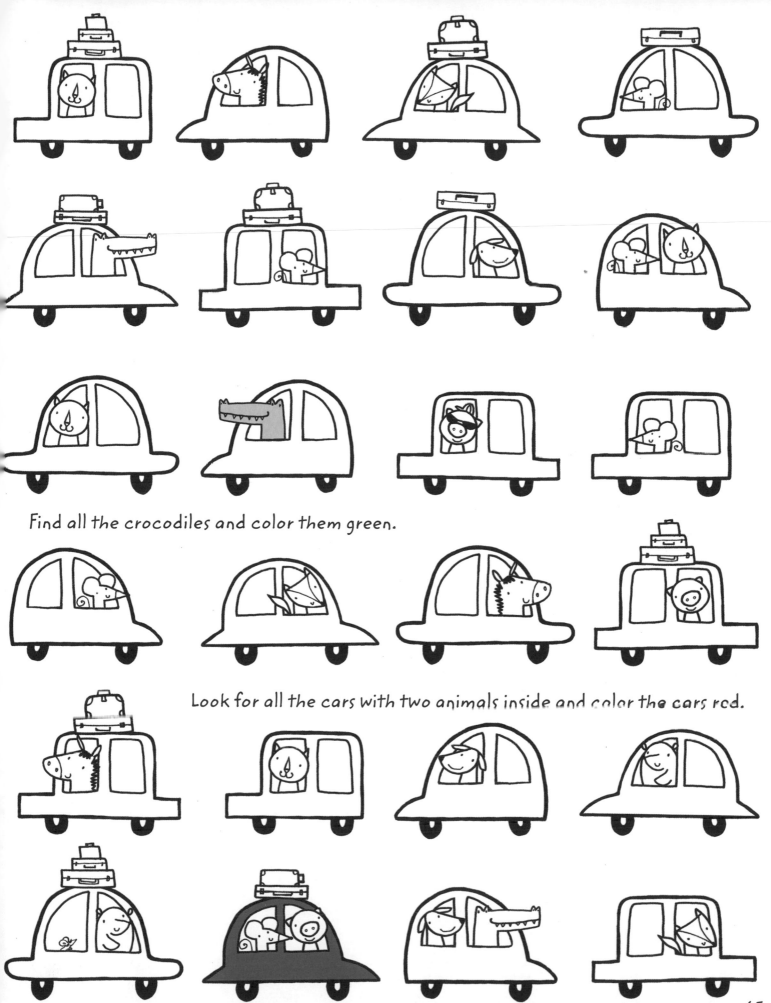

Find all the crocodiles and color them green.

Look for all the cars with two animals inside and color the cars red.

65

This rabbit is wearing sunglasses. Can you spot five more?

Find five rabbits taking photographs.

Find five more blue birds like this.

Can you spot the rabbits holding white balloons? Color in the balloons.

Here's a rollerskating rabbit, find five more.

67

Find the boats with sails and color the sails red.

Spot the boats with three round windows and color the boats blue.

Find all the boats with bent funnels and color the funnels orange.

Can you spot the boat with an anchor? Color it yellow.

69

Follow the lines of smoke to find out which plane has just taken off. Color it in.

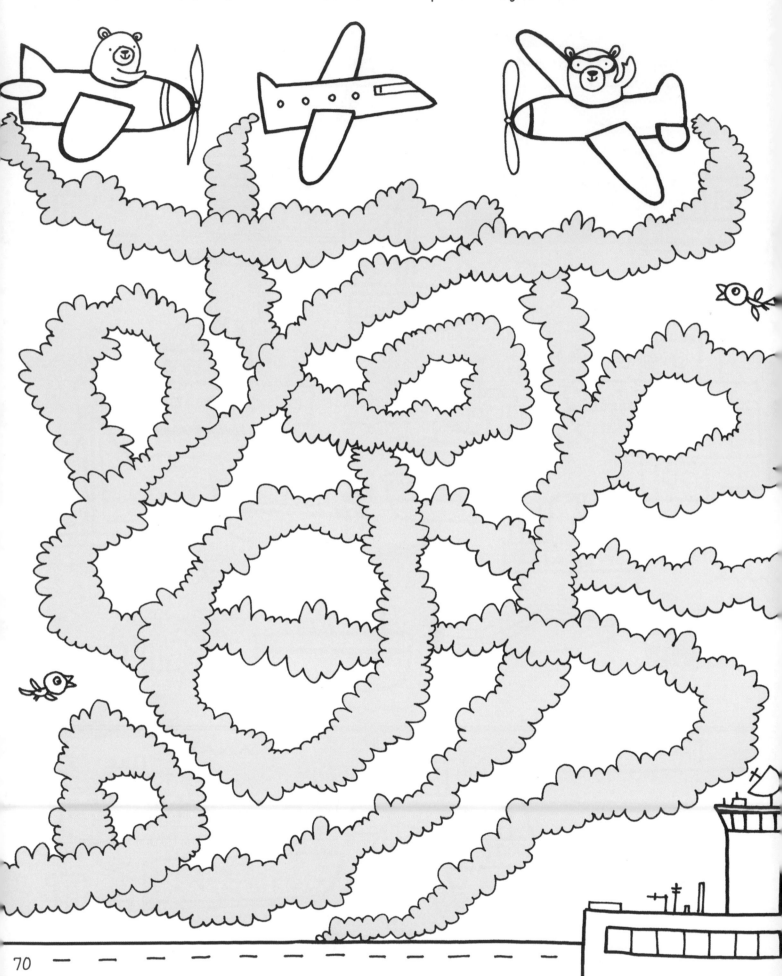

Find two souvenirs that are exactly the same. Color them to match.

Color in all the souvenir keyrings.

Color in the souvenir from Australia.

Find and color the rabbits hiding among the bears.

Can you spot the panda?

Find and color five more bears eating cupcakes.

72

Color in all the bears that are eating sandwiches.

Spot the bear playing a guitar.

73

Sunshine Villas

Draw people inside all the empty windows.

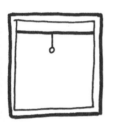

Look for a cat, then color it in.

74

SeaView

HOLIDAY APARTMENTS

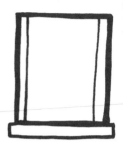

Find six people wearing hats and color them in.

Find the people wearing sunglasses and color them in.

Color in the elephant.

Find the people eating ice cream cones and color them in.

Color in all the things that someone might take on a picnic.

Look for all the wasps with no stripes and draw some on them.

Can you spot the wasp wearing a bow tie?

Color all the wasps yellow.

Find all the balloons and color them red.

Find and color the mice wearing sunglasses.

78

Can you spot a mouse playing a saxophone?

Color in all the little mice in bicycle trailers.

79

Can you spot five red ladybugs?

Look for five bugs wearing black hats.

80

Spot the bug holding a watering can.

Find five green bugs, like this.

Color in all the snails' shells.

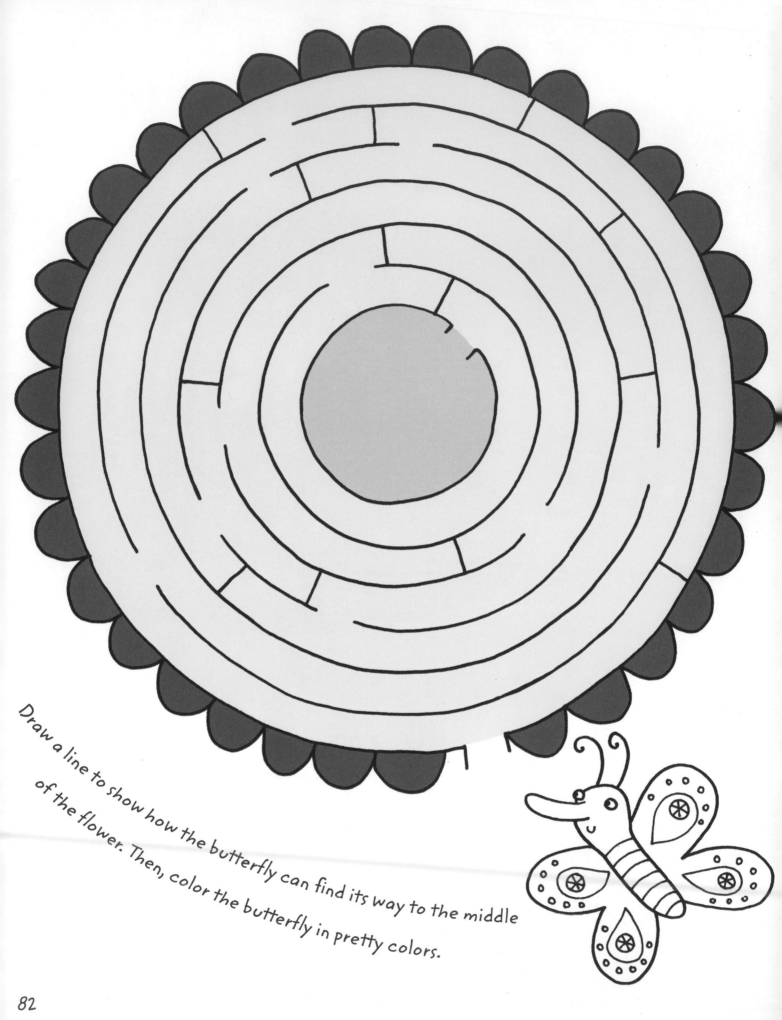

Draw a line to show how the butterfly can find its way to the middle of the flower. Then, color the butterfly in pretty colors.

Find the cacti with three flowers and color the flowers pink.

   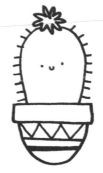  

Color in all the pots with spots on them.

   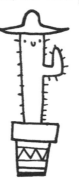  

Find the cacti with no flowers and color them green.

Can you spot a cactus wearing a hat?

    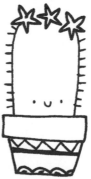 

83

Find all the animals holding popsicles and color the popsicles pink.

Color in the cat who has dropped its ice cream.

Can you find and color the cat wearing sunglasses?

Draw some more animals eating ice creams.

Mr Ice

Find all the snails hiding in this picture. Draw spirals on their shells like this.

Can you spot tiny ladybugs hiding too? Color them red.

Find and color all the flowers that look like this.

Follow the luggage chutes to find out which one goes to the plane.

Find and color all the strawberries, like this.

Color all the slices of lemon yellow.

Can you spot five more black ants like this on the fruit?

89

Find the tents with two pigs inside and color them orange.

Look for all the pigs wearing rain boots and color them in.

Find the little rabbit hiding behind a tent and color it.

Color the tents with one bear in red.

Find the bears wearing hats and color them in.

Look for all the crabs playing drums and color them in.

Color in all the fish playing a trumpet.

Can you spot two fish playing guitars?

93

Find the sand castles with shells and color them yellow.

Color all the flags in bright colors.

Find four crabs hiding among the sand castles. Color them in red.

94

Find and color two butterfly kites.

Which two kites are the same? Color them in.

Find all the moles wearing glasses and color them in.

Color all the bees yellow.

Can you spot the hole with two moles peeking out?

First published in 2011 by Usborne Publishing Ltd.,
83-85 Saffron Hill, London, EC1N 8RT, England. www.usborne.com
Copyright © 2011 Usborne Publishing Ltd. The name Usborne and the devices 🎈 🌐 are Trade Marks of Usborne Publishing Ltd.
All rights reserved. No part of this publication may be reproduced, stored in a retrieval system, or transmitted in any form
or by any means, electronic, mechanical, photocopy, recording or otherwise, without prior permission of the publisher.
AE First published in America 2015.